JUST JAZZ

Progressive piano solos

BY STEPHEN DURO

Chester Music

(A division of Music Sales Limited)
8/9 Frith Street
London WIV 5TZ

PREFACE

Here are 14 songs carefully chosen from the repertory of jazz 'standards'. Playing these arrangments calls for particular interpretative skills; here are a few suggestions to help your performance.

Rhythmical numbers should aim to set the foot tapping. In many cases this can be achieved by subtly accentuating the second and fourth beats in a bar. Groups of even quavers ♫♫ should generally be played as if written ♪𝄾♪𝄾 - known as 'swung'. On the other hand, songs in slow tempi should be played 'straight' (with even quavers) more often than not. Some of the ballads make use of rich harmonies and all such passages should be unhurried.

The songs are arranged according to difficulty, with the easier pieces (approximately Grade II standard of the Associated Board) appearing first, and the harder ones (Grade V/VI standard) towards the end. Fingering, where indicated, is intended as a guide only and should be altered to suit the needs of individual players.

Stephen Duro

This book © Copyright 1996 Chester Music
Order No. CH61057 ISBN 0-7119-4376-1

Music processed by Stephen Duro.
Cover design by 4i Limited.
Printed in the United Kingdom by Caligraving Limited Thetford Norfolk

CONTENTS

FLY ME TO THE MOON

Words and music by Bart Howard

Originally written as a waltz, this song has long been a favourite of jazz instrumentalists. Try accenting the second beat of the melody (in bars 5 and 7, for example) as this contributes to a 'groovy' effect.

I'M BEGINNING TO SEE THE LIGHT

Words and music by Harry James, Duke Ellington,
Johnny Hodges and Don George

Some of the 'swingy' phrases, for example the opening bass line, have been written as crochets followed by semiquavers, but in other instances the phrasing has been left to the discretion of the performer.

I'LL REMEMBER APRIL

Words and music by Don Raye, Gene de Paul
and Patricia Johnson

The long melodic lines in this classic ballad will benefit
from being played in a gentle, unhurried manner. The
dynamic range need never rise above a *mezzo forte*.

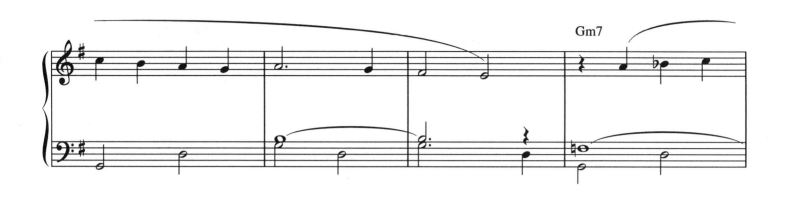

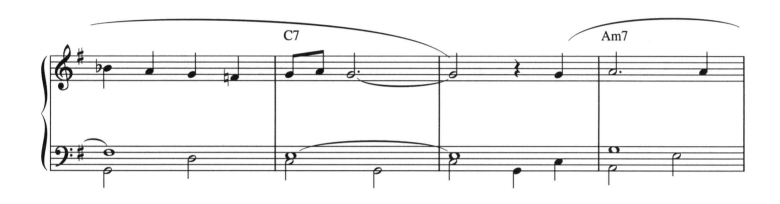

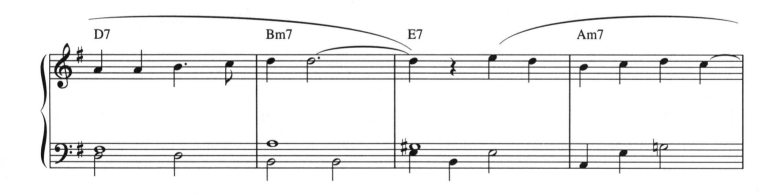

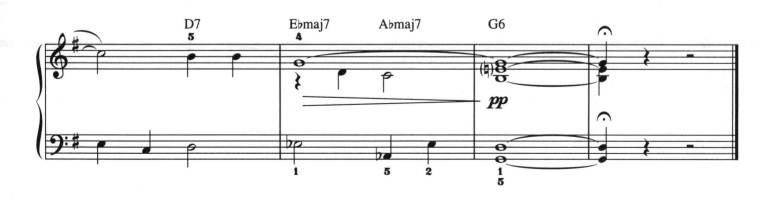

CARAVAN

By Duke Ellington, Irving Mills and Juan Tizol

This arrangement depends on good rhythmical control, especially in the left hand. The tempo indication 'moderately fast' can be modified to 'not too fast' at the discretion of the performer.

MANHATTAN SPIRITUAL

By Billy Maxted

A piece which is reminiscent of those hand-clapping gospel songs. The performer should try to evoke the happy yet fervent atmosphere.

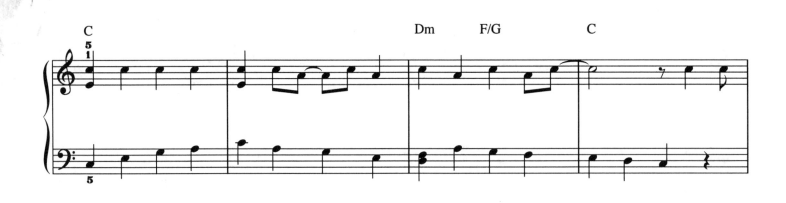

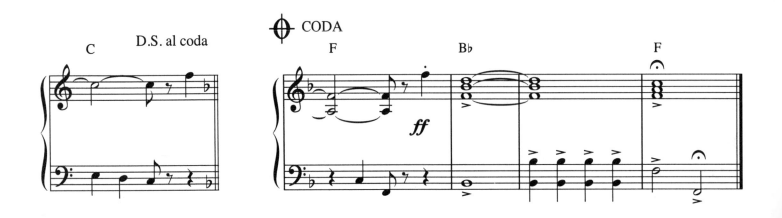

HERE'S THAT RAINY DAY

Words by Johnny Burke and music by Jimmy Van Heusen

To be played gently throughout. The tune, as well as the counter-melodies in the left hand, should be slightly accentuated, and the chordal passages as in bar 6 should be unhurried.

TAKE THE 'A' TRAIN

Words and music by Billy Strayhorn

A piece made famous by the Duke Ellington Orchestra. The tune needs to be stated boldly with strong accents on the fourth and eighth quavers in the tenth bar.

LI'L DARLIN'

Words by Bart Howard and music by Neal Hefti

This piece demands a totally relaxed style of playing whilst keeping the semblance of a beat going. The quaver passages, notably beginning at bar 12, should have a $\frac{12}{8}$ feel.

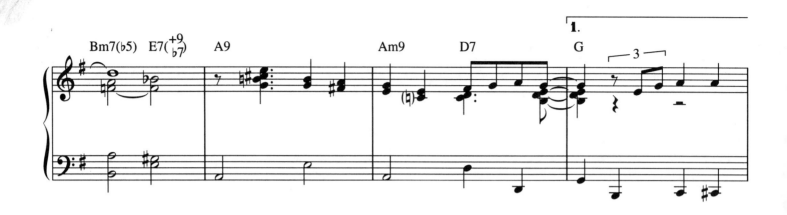

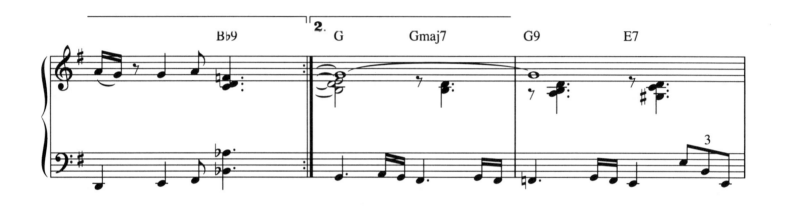

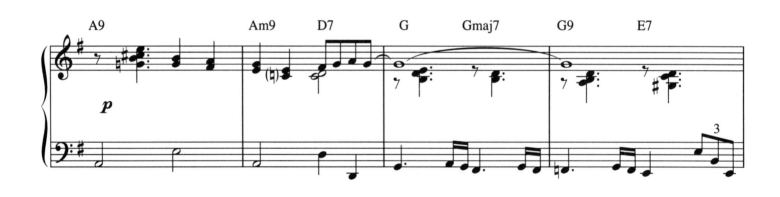

FASCINATING RHYTHM

Music and lyrics by George Gershwin and Ira Gershwin

The subtlety of this song derives from the initial motif which is twice repeated with effective rhythmical displacement. An accent on the last quaver of the third group of six notes will enhance the general effect.

CHELSEA BRIDGE

By Billy Strayhorn

The composer of this haunting ballad was for many years a musical associate of the legendary Duke Ellington. The arrangement requires quiet, atmospheric playing throughout.

CUTE

Words by Stanley Styne and music by Neal Hefti

This piece was originally conceived as an interchange between drums and band. Here, the drum 'fills' are assigned to the right and left hands. It should be played in a light-hearted manner.

34

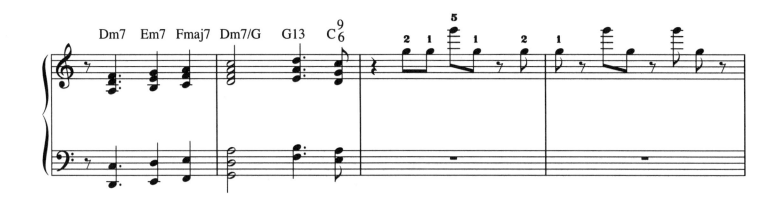

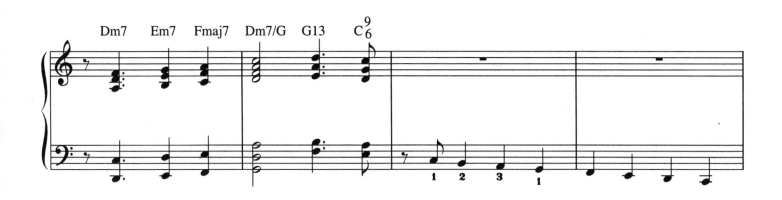

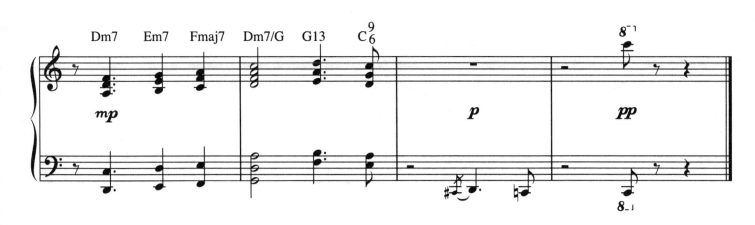

BERNIE'S TUNE

By Bernie Miller

This is a classic of the 'cool' repertoire. A feature of the 'cool' style of playing is that the music should have a feeling of restraint and power held in reserve.

LULLABY OF BIRDLAND

Words by George David Weiss and music by George Shearing

This tune combines both even quavers, as in bars 5 and 9, and 'swung' quavers, i.e. notes with a $\frac{12}{8}$ feel. The arrangement should sound smooth and relaxed throughout.

A NIGHT IN TUNISIA

Words by Raymond Leveen and music by Frank Paparelli
and Dizzy Gillespie

This tune needs strong, rhythmical playing in the left
hand in order to bring out its exotic character.

11/96 (26386)